JEREMY CORBYN!

Annual 2019

JC ★ ALWAYS 100% UNOFFICIAL

ADAM G GOODWIN

DICKEN GOODWIN

JONATHAN PARKYN

JEREMY CORByN!

Annual 2019

First published in the United Kingdom in 2018 by

Portico
43 Great Ormond Street
London
WC1N 3HZ

An imprint of Pavilion Books Company Ltd
Copyright © Pavilion Books Company Ltd 2018
Text copyright © Yes/No Publishing Services 2018

ISBN 978-1-91162-209-3

A CIP catalogue record for this book is available from the British Library.

10 9 8 7 6 5 4 3 2 1

Reproduction by Rival Colour Ltd, UK
Printed and bound by G. Canale & C. S.p.A., Italy

This book can be ordered direct from the publisher at
www.pavilionbooks.com

This book belongs to.

Name ....

Age ....

packed full of Fruity Corbyn Goodness!

CONTENTS!

CONTENTS!

GREETINGS EARTHLETS!

It's the editor here! What another fab-u-lous year for JC, and that can only mean another totally wunderbar edition of every good socialist's favourite book – THE UNOFFICIAL JEREMY CORBYN ANNUAL 2019. We had so much fun putting this together that we almost literally went interstellar, and so you may notice a little bit of stardust sprinkled onto some of these pages. In fact, if you are looking to go on a fun-fuelled, fun-filled journey jetting off into the stratosphere, with Captain Corbyn at the helm, then look no further than this annual!

Inside you will find Mystic Jeremy's Horoscopes for 2019, Corbyn Trek – The Search for Words(search), cosmic crosswords, Jezza's Celestial Party Snacks, Corbyn's Space-Craft Corner, and more fun puzzles and games than you can shake a sonic screwdriver at! Not only this, but also you will find sizzling photostories Possessed by Love and A Conservative Affair, the discombobulating adventure The Red Planet and the seriously raunchy A Revolutionary Romance. With super fun masks of Boris Johnson and JC, dreamy pics of you know who, Comrades of the Left Beard-Grooming Tips, A Corbyn for All Seasons guide to the year's holidays and a whole galaxy of other great treats and surprises for all.

To infinity and beyond!

The Editor

REES-MOGGIES ON THE LOOSE GAME

Oh no! In a bid to wipe out the Labour Party those evil Tories have let loose some Rees-Moggies to hunt down their socialist prey! Cat-catcher Corbyn has already caught the main Rees-Moggie but can you help him round up the remaining right-wing feline foe before they succeed?

CAT CATCHER CORBYN

Hidden throughout the pages of this annual are twelve Rees-Moggies. Find them and circle them, then return to Jeremy on the answers page with a final figure of how many you caught.

JEREMY'S ALIENIZER
DISGUISE KIT

INTERSTELLAR FREEDOM FIGHTER, JEREMY CORBYN, IS ON A MISSION TO UNCOVER SOCIAL INJUSTICE AND CORRUPTION ACROSS THE GALAXY! HELP HIM TO INFILTRATE PLANETS WHERE CAPITALISM IS RIFE BY USING A SERIES OF CUNNING ALIEN DISGUISES. CUT OUT THE ALIEN BODY PARTS BELOW AND STICK THEM ONTO THE PHOTO OF JEREMY — THEN SEND HIM DEEP UNDERCOVER!

1 THE BULBOUS EYEBALL STALKS OF A VENUSIAN SPACE SLUG.

2 THE DEADLY CLAWS OF A RAVENOUS THUG BEAST FROM THE THIRD MOON OF KSKAAAKAKKLAVAN.

3 THE POISONOUS TENTACLES OF A SILARIAN SLIMEBALL.

4 THE THIRD EAR-STOMACH FROM AN AURORAN ASTRAL COW.

5 THE HEAD-BUTT OF ONE OF THE FLATULENT SPACE MONKS OF ANTILLES.

6 THE BLONDE MOP-HAIR FROM BORIS JOHNSON.

LEGEND HAS IT THAT IN THE EARLY DAYS OF SOCIALISM, THIS VASE WAS WROUGHT FROM THE BONES OF DOWNTRODDEN WORKERS, FORCED INTO HARD LABOUR BY AN EVIL CAPITALIST – THE STEAM-POWERED INDUSTRIALIST, SIR MANDRAKE FORTESCUE. BUT ONE DAY, HIS WORKERS REVOLTED, OVERTHROWING THEIR MASTER AND TRAPPING HIS SOUL IN THE VASE FOR ALL ETERNITY…

IT'S SAID THAT WHOEVER OWNS THE VASE WILL BE POSSESSED BY FORTESCUE'S EVIL SOUL. IT'S PROBABLY A LOAD OF OLD BOILED GRAVY, BUT I DON'T WANT TO TAKE ANY CHANCES.

I DIDN'T BELIEVE ANY OF THAT!

I THINK IT'S JUST A PRETTY VASE THAT I CAN PUT IN MY BEDSIT, FOR FLOWERS.

NO! YOU MUST NEVER DO THAT! I AM THE VASE'S CUSTODIAN AND IT MUST NEVER LEAVE MY SIGHT, EXCEPT IF I NEED A WEE.

IT'S ALSO SAID THAT THE VASE MUST NEVER UNDER ANY CIRCUMSTANCES BE PLACED ON AN OCCASIONAL TABLE AND WHATEVER YOU DO, NEVER, EVER, EVER, EVER POLISH IT WITH A DUSTER

I DON'T CARE. I JUST WANT IT.

I REALLY, REALLY WANT IT. PLEASE?

WELL… OKAY, THEN. YOU'VE PUT UP A GOOD ARGUMENT. I'LL LET YOU BUY THE CURSED VASE ON ONE CONDITION…

… TO MAKE SURE YOU DON'T GET POSSESSED I'LL HAVE TO FOLLOW YOU AROUND, WHEREVER YOU GO. EXCEPT WHEN I NEED A WEE.

DEAL! LET'S HOPE YOU DON'T NEED A WEE JUST WHEN I'M BEING POSSESSED! HAHAHAHA!

Debbie had made a joke.

Jeremy helped Debbie walk homewards…

I COULD GET USED TO A HUNKY LABOUR MP FOLLOWING ME AROUND!

Back at Debbie's bedsit, Jeremy nipped to the loo for a wee…

NOW, FIRST THINGS FIRST. LET'S PUT THIS VASE ON MY OCCASIONAL TABLE.

Later on in the park, they sat by a tree…

OOH! SUDDENLY I DON'T FEEL VERY WELL… AS IF SOME KIND OF VICTORIAN HAS TAKEN HOLD OF ME!

ARE YOU OKAY, DEBBIE? YOU LOOK A BIT POSSESSED.

FLIP OFF, YOU IDIOT!

11

OH NO! THAT'S SIR MANDRAKE FORTESCUE'S VOICE! YOU MUST'VE BROKEN THE RULES WHILE I WAS WEEING!

YOUR FLIPPING MOTHER SUCKS BOILED EGGS IN HELL, YOU SOCIALIST BUMBUM!

Jeremy picked up Debbie by her arm.

He held her firmly by the shoulder.

DON'T FLIPPING TOUCH ME, YOU FLIPPING IDIOT! STICK YOUR STUPID SCARF UP YOUR SOCIALIST BUM AND BUZZ OFF!

THERE'S NOTHING FOR IT – I'VE GOT TO EXORCISE HER!

THE POWER OF MARX COMPELS YOU! LEAVE THIS GIRL, SIR FORTESCUE!

WINKLE BUM WILLIE POO-POO!!

As a last resort, Jeremy sucked the evil entity out of Debbie's mouth.

PHEW! I CAN FEEL THE CAPITALISM LEAVING ME!

Back at Debbie's bedsit, Jeremy needed another wee...

WHILE JEREMY'S ON THE LOO I'LL JUST GIVE MY VASE A QUICK POLISH WITH A DUSTER.

Later, by a shop...

I PROMISE, JEREMY. I'M COMPLETELY FINE NOW.

GOOD, BECAUSE...

HOLD ON... WHAT'S THIS FUNNY FEELING I'VE GOT IN MY TUMMY?

MAYBE IT'S JUST WIND? PLEASE TELL ME YOU DIDN'T POLISH THE VASE WITH A DUSTER!

WEASEL FANNY BOOB MAN PUT YOUR FLIPPING SOCIALIST SCARF UP YOUR BUMBUM!

OH NO, NOT AGAIN! REMEMBER, JEREMY, IT'S NOT DEBBIE TELLING YOU TO PUT YOUR SCARF UP YOUR BUMBUM...

...IT'S SIR FORTESCUE. AND I'M GOING TO HAVE TO SUCK HIM OUT OF DEBBIE AGAIN. THIS TIME IN FRONT OF A SHOP!

YOUR FACE IS LIKE A DOG POO!

Later, after Jeremy had sucked her again...

HOW COULD I BE SUCH A NITWIT? SAYING RUDE WORDS AND BEING POSSESSED BY A VASE IS SO UN-SOCIALIST!

She went outside...

I REALISE NOW! IT WASN'T THE VASE I LOVED...

...IT WAS THE VASE'S BEARDED CUSTODIAN! WHY DIDN'T I SEE IT?

Back at Labour Antiques...

LOOK, LOVE, IF YOU'RE POSSESSED AGAIN, THEN FORGET ABOUT IT. I'VE SUCKED YOU TWICE NOW AND I'VE GOT THESE FILTHY WINDOWS TO CLEAN.

BUT...

...LOOK, JEREMY, I'VE GOT A BIT OF A CONFESSION TO MAKE.

CONFESS AWAY!

It was time to tell the truth...

...Debbie stood near Jeremy.

I GOT POSSESSED ON PURPOSE. I KNEW THAT IF I WAS POSSESSED YOU WOULD SUCK THE SPIRIT OUT OF ME. I USED A SUPERNATURAL PHENOMENON TO GET CLOSE TO YOU AND NOW I FEEL DIRTY.

YOU USED MY KINDFULNESS AGAINST ME. THAT WAS WRONG. AS GUARDIAN OF THE VASE, MY COMMITMENT IS UNWAVERING. CAN YOU DROP IT BACK TO ME LATER, PLEASE?

I SUPPOSE I DESERVE THAT. I PROMISE I'LL NEVER POSSESS MYSELF AGAIN.

That night, Debbie had a restless sleep...

MANDRAKE... VASE... JEREMY... OCCASIONAL... DUSTER... DIRTY WINDOW... BUMBUMS...

...And when she woke, the vase was smashed into eleven pieces.

MY VASE IS BROKEN AND I AM BROKEN, TOO, LIKE A CURSED VASE, FALLEN FROM A SHELF IN THE LABOUR ANTIQUE SHOP OF LIFE!

THE END

13

HYPAFAX 2104

JEREMY CORBYN

WARP SPEED (LIGHT YEARS)	1.26(PH)
HOME PLANET	EARTH
NEMESIS LIFEFORM	THE THATCHERITES
THREAT TO UNIVERSE	0.6GB
HYPER-GUILE	ADEQUATE
BINARY REFERENCE	1100101010
WAR CRY	NONE
FEDER-RATING	98

CORBYN BY NUMBERS

Legend: ① 1 · ② 2 · ③ 3 · ④ 4 · ⑤ 5 · ⑥ 6 · ⑦ 7 · ⑧ 8

2	2	2	2	2	2	2	2	2	2	2	2	2
2	2	2	2	2	2	2	2	2	2	1	2	2
2	2	2	7	7	7	7	7	7	7	3	3	1
2	2	7	7	7	7	7	7	7	7	7	3	1
2	1	7	7	7	7	7	7	7	7	7	1	1
1	1	7	7	7	7	7	7	7	7	7	1	1
1	3	8	8	8	8	8	8	8	8	8	1	
1	3		8	8	8	8	8	8	8		1	
1	1					4					1	1
1	4		4	7	4	4	4	7	4		4	1
1	4		6	4	4	4	4	4	6		4	1
1	1										1	1
2	1					5					1	1
2	1										1	2
2	2	1								1	2	2
2	2	1								2	2	2
2	1	1	1	1	1	1	1	1	2	1	1	2
1	1	1	2	2	1	2	2	2	2	1	1	1

I DREAM of JEREMY

Have you ever wondered what your dreams might mean? Experts believe that dreams are unconscious reflections of our inner preoccupations, fears and desires. And, if Jeremy Corbyn was an expert, he'd almost certainly believe that too. Below are some of our readers' dreams, along with the expert analysis that Jeremy Corbyn would have given if he was an expert, and if he had used the latest Labour Manifesto to answer the readers' questions. Let Dream Doctor Jeremy interpret all your wildest dreams!

Learning a lesson

Dear Dream Doctor Jeremy,

Last night I had a dream where I went back to my old school, but I was naked and couldn't find any clothes to put on. Everyone laughed at me and it was really embarrassing. A couple of weeks ago, I went back to my old school in real life, but I was naked and couldn't find any clothes to put on. I'm wondering whether the two things might be connected?

Tommy,

Scunthorpe

Jez Sez

Hi Tommy.

No, I don't think the two are connected in any way. In fact, I think your dream might be related to deep-seated fears about the education policies of the current Conservative government. Governments have the responsibility to make lifelong learning a reality by giving everyone the opportunity to access education throughout their lives. To meet this responsibility, Labour will create a unified National Education Service (NES) for England to move towards cradle-to-grave learning that is free at the point of use. The NES will be built on the principle that 'Every Child – and Adult – Matters' and will incorporate all forms of education, from early years through to adult education. Might I suggest voting Labour at the next general election to prevent your fears coming true?

Room for improvement

Dear Dream Doctor Jeremy,

I have a recurring dream where I keep finding extra rooms in my house – sometimes behind a door I never knew was there and sometimes I discover a whole basement floor under my stairs. My theory is that it's my subconscious telling me I need my own space. I am the mother of sextuplets and my husband is always 'too busy' to help.

Laura,

Peterborough

Fly, fly away

Dear Dream Doctor Jeremy,

I know everyone has dreams that they can fly, but mine feel really real. In my dreams, if I flap my feet and hands really, really hard, I can raise myself off the ground by about half a foot. Then, if I lean forward I can waft along, 'steering' myself by leaning my shoulders. It feels so real in my dreams that I had to try it out in real life after a visit to my local pub. Unfortunately, I sprained my ankle trying to 'fly' off my mum's Toyota and ended up in A&E all night.

Jace,

Nuneaton

Sounds unusual

Dear Dream Doctor Jeremy,

I know that some people dream in colour, some dream only in black and white. But I dream in only sounds – mostly high bpm Detroit techno, breakbeat hardcore and acid trance – and I would like to know why.

Russ

Plymouth

PS – I did a lot of drugs in the early 90s rave scene. Don't know if relevant.

Jez Sez

My suspicion is that you're subconsciously stressed about the shortage of social housing in the UK. I don't know whether you live in social housing (you don't say) but, under the Conservatives, affordable housebuilding has fallen to a 24-year low. That's enough to cause anyone sleepless nights! Labour will build the genuinely affordable homes to rent and buy that the country needs. We'll remove government restrictions that stop councils building homes and begin the biggest council building programme for at least 30 years. Vote Labour and your dreams could come true.

Jez Sez

Yes, Jace. The National Health Service is overstretched, isn't it? Successive governments have failed the NHS, leading to chronic underfunding and a shortage of skilled doctors and nurses. Labour will invest in our NHS, to give patients the modern, well-resourced services they need for the 21st century. Labour will ensure that NHS patients get the world-class quality of care they need and that staff are able to deliver the standards that patients expect. Austerity isn't working – let's vote the Tories out.

Jez Sez

The economy, you say? Yes, Labour's economic strategy is about delivering a fairer, more prosperous society for the many, not just the few. Labour understands that the creation of wealth is a collective endeavour between workers, entrepreneurs, investors and government – all of whom contribute and all of whom must share fairly in the rewards. That's why we plan to upgrade our economy and rewrite the rules of a rigged system, so that our economy really works – for everyone. Vote Labour.

M A R X U E W S L E G N E
C Z J Y T A S T E R O I D
O S H R O P S H I R E F U
R X S W P W F S B E A R D
B L K M I D A O I E E Q C
Y I R I A B P C W C D N Y
N N M S I L A I C O S A M
S E L E F T H E S N K I E
C N R O C K E T E O I B R
E T U J V T W Y E M N A E
J A M I L L E T R Y D F J
P R O L E T A R I A T O D
M O G G M W E L F A R E V

CORBYN TREK
THE SEARCH FOR WORDS

The ruthless Torusians from the planet Capitalanus are frightened of Captain Jeremy's attempts to spread socialism throughout the galaxy. They've stolen his favourite words and dispersed them around the Universe hoping that Captain Jeremy won't be able to advance his message and boldly go where no opposition leader has gone before. Find the missing words and help Captain Jeremy continue his mission.

PROLETARIAT JEREMY ASTEROID
SHROPSHIRE MILLET WELFARE ECONOMY
BEARD SOCIALISM REES ROCKET MARX KIND
UTOPIA FABIAN LINEN CORBYN MOGG JAM
JUTE LEFT ENGELS SOCIETY

CORBYN'S SPACE-CRAFT CORNER

When Jeremy isn't leading the Labour Party he probably likes to spend his time getting busy with the foolscap, tape and scissors. And what he'd possibly like to create is a real-life, working space capsule to send information about himself to other socialist species across the galaxy. Now you can do that too! Just follow the instructions and send your message to the stars.

WHAT YOU WILL NEED:

FELT TIPS OR CRAYONS

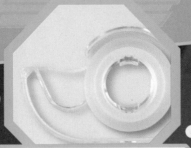

STICKY TAPE

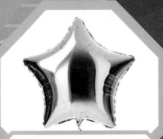

A HELIUM BALLOON FULL OF HELIUM

BLUNT-TIP SCISSORS

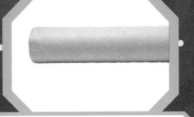

A KITCHEN-ROLL TUBE

SOME SILVER COOKING FOIL

A PHOTOGRAPH OF JEREMY
[perhaps from a parent's magazine or newspaper... or even from this annual!]

ANOTHER PHOTOGRAPH, BUT OF YOURSELF

1. Take your kitchen-roll tube and cover it in kitchen foil to create the 'fuselage' and 'cockpit' of the capsule. Stick the foil to the tube using the sticky tape.

2. Use the tape to seal one end of the tube.

3. Now stick the photograph of Jeremy to the fuselage using the glitter sticky tape.

4. With your felt tips write the name of your capsule on the fuselage. Be as adventurous as you can be. Remember we're speaking to aliens so we want to seem as exciting and socially responsible a species as we can be. Some examples might be 'SS Equal Enterprise' or simply 'Jeremy.'

5. Now fill the capsule with small, light items that you feel will represent you to an alien race. A feather from your budgerigar for example or a lock of your beard.

6. Now fill out the form over the page and insert it into your cockpit, to give those Bolshevik beings as much info about you as possible.

7. Finally, stick the helium balloon full of helium to the fuselage and prepare for takeoff!

GOOD LUCK
AND MAY THE JEREMY BE WITH YOU

SPACE CAPTAIN
CORBYN'S MATE

My astronaut name is:

....

My astronaut age is:

....

My spaceship is called:

....

Jeremy Corbyn is my favourite space captain because:

....

....

My favourite vacuum-packed food-paste is:

....

My favourite space-sport team is:

....

My galactic political policies are:

....

HYPAFAX 9534

JOHN MCDONNELL

WARP SPEED (LIGHT YEARS)	0.72(PH)
HOME PLANET	VULCAN
NEMESIS LIFEFORM	TRIBBLES
THREAT TO UNIVERSE	8.3GB
HYPER-GUILE	PROFICIENT
BINARY REFERENCE	11111101
WAR CRY	NASHIV-TOR!
FEDER-RATING	28

A CORBYN
FOR ALL SEASONS

An alternative, non-denominational guide to the year ahead for Corbyn supporters, young and old

Spring

It's spring time. The buds are appearing on the trees, the lambs are frolicking in the meadows, and love is in the air. On St Corbyntine's Day we secretly celebrate those closest to our hearts. With red roses to symbolise both our love and our love of the Labour Party.

As the season progresses, we start looking forward to Corbyn Easter, when the Corbynista Bunny distributes an equal amount of Fairtrade chocolate to children everywhere.

Summer

On the last Sunday of every March, British Corbyn Time officially begins. The days grow longer and warmer and we start looking forward to the parliamentary summer recess.

The bees buzz and the butterflies flutter, and soon it will be the Corbyn Solstice – the longest day of the year. Once the busy summer festival season is in full swing, Jeremy can usually be found onstage being regaled by crowds of adoring young festival-goers.

Autumn

The orange and yellow leaves are falling from the trees. Our allotments have been harvested. And we start to enjoy crunchy walks in forests and parks. But as the nights get darker, we brace ourselves for the terror of Jerroween, where we celebrate the socialist spirits and left-wing ghosts of the past. Children dressed as Engels, Marx, Castro and Benn can be seen roaming the streets, spreading goodwill.

Then, on Cor-bonfire Night, faces light up with joy from fireworks displays across the land celebrating the life of British diplomat turned Soviet agent, Guy Burgess.

Winter

There's a chill in the air. A white frost covers the land. And we all wrap up warm to keep ourselves healthy so that we don't overstretch the NHS.

In December our thoughts turn to celebrations. For soon it will be Jezzmas Day – a time for family, food and fond socialist reflection.

Merry Jezzmas, everyone!

JEREMY'S "QUEST FOR ADVENTURE" ADVENTURE

I — You are a normal, kind-hearted, bearded human growing up on the cruel streets of Shropshire. You have little to your name other than the clothes on your back, a single gobstopper, some gardening twine from your allotment and a burgeoning notion that you want to share things with other people. But one day an evil capitalist alien called Crudo arrives in his time-craft from the future. Only YOU can see Crudo. Crudo has been sent from the 'Further Time' to squeeze the public services of money and privatise them with his mind-calibration machine. You have two choices – do you grab Crudo by the scruff of his scaly neck and march him off to the Time Police Station at Telford (go to 2)? Or do you set up a disciplinary court in your bedroom to deal with the pungent, scaly chrono-reptile yourself (go to 3)?

2 — On the way to the Time Police Station you are caught unawares by Crudo, who manages to escape and climb on to his hover chariot. But before Crudo can slip away, you use your gardening twine to lasso yourself to the safety rail of his levitating vehicle and get pulled forward to the 'Further Time' through a Time Hole. Once in the 'Further Time' you succeed in danger-diving from the flying craft and perform a stunt-roll into a future-bush, without ruining your linen jacket. You look around. The 'Further Time' is a barren place where all the goodness has been sucked out by centuries of austerity. To your left is the Time Hole and to your right is Crudo counting his stolen human money. Do you dive into the Time Hole before it closes and return to the 'Now Time' (go to 5)? Or do you creep up on the unsuspecting extraterrestrial and deal out some justice to him with a knuckle sandwich with the intention of returning to the 'Now Time' and redistributing Crudo's ill-gotten sterling amongst the poor (go to 4)?

3 — Crudo escapes your homemade cuffs of gardening twine and mercilessly grinds your brain in his human skull grinder to create himself a tasty human brain-smoothie to drink. Your adventure ends here.

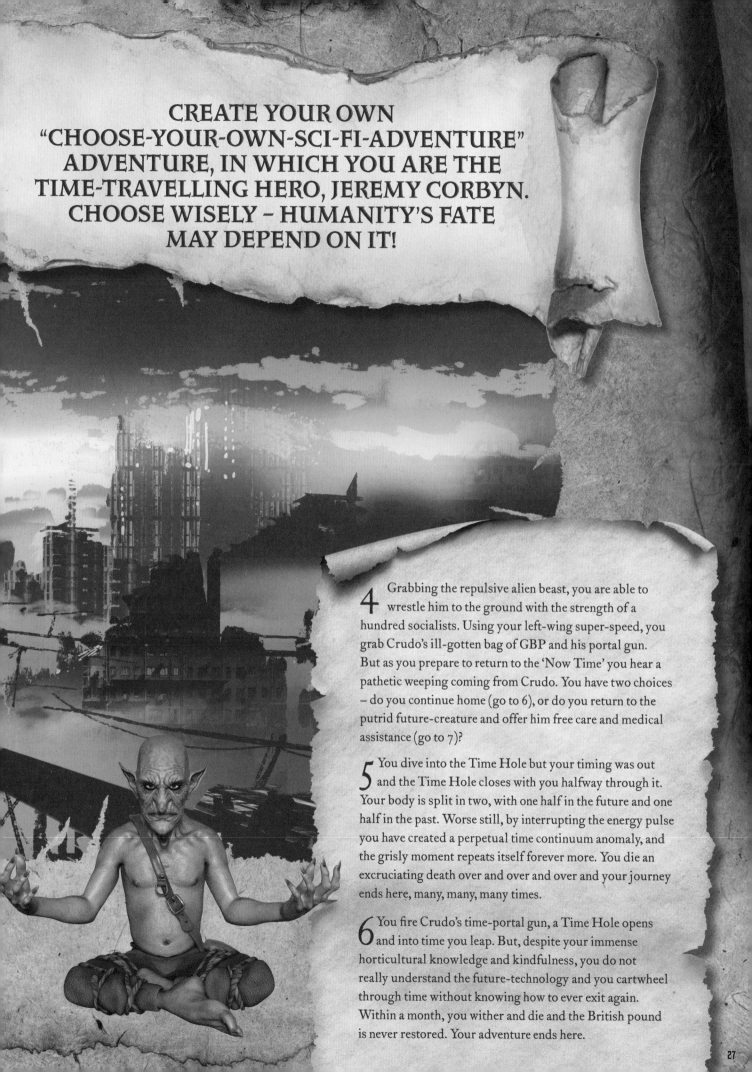

CREATE YOUR OWN
"CHOOSE-YOUR-OWN-SCI-FI-ADVENTURE"
ADVENTURE, IN WHICH YOU ARE THE
TIME-TRAVELLING HERO, JEREMY CORBYN.
CHOOSE WISELY – HUMANITY'S FATE
MAY DEPEND ON IT!

4 Grabbing the repulsive alien beast, you are able to wrestle him to the ground with the strength of a hundred socialists. Using your left-wing super-speed, you grab Crudo's ill-gotten bag of GBP and his portal gun. But as you prepare to return to the 'Now Time' you hear a pathetic weeping coming from Crudo. You have two choices – do you continue home (go to 6), or do you return to the putrid future-creature and offer him free care and medical assistance (go to 7)?

5 You dive into the Time Hole but your timing was out and the Time Hole closes with you halfway through it. Your body is split in two, with one half in the future and one half in the past. Worse still, by interrupting the energy pulse you have created a perpetual time continuum anomaly, and the grisly moment repeats itself forever more. You die an excruciating death over and over and over and your journey ends here, many, many, many times.

6 You fire Crudo's time-portal gun, a Time Hole opens and into time you leap. But, despite your immense horticultural knowledge and kindfulness, you do not really understand the future-technology and you cartwheel through time without knowing how to ever exit again. Within a month, you wither and die and the British pound is never restored. Your adventure ends here.

7 You return to Crudo and, despite his feeble tears, you pick him up and show him great compassion. You remove your handkerchief from your linen trousers and dab the tears from his leathery face. Once his pitiful wailing has subsided, Crudo explains that in the 'Further Time' he is a slave and is forced to work for an evil empress called Empress Terrorsa-may. It is Empress Terrorsa-may who has become immensely rich by collecting all the sterling from the past in a bid to undermine the 'Now Time' economy and rule via an economic system based upon private ownership of the means of production, and their operation for profit. You are furious at this injustice and vow to correct this deplorable imbalance. You explain to Crudo the principles of socialism and the simple soul seems pleased at what he hears. But Crudo explains that Terrorsa-may is very powerful and to challenge her would mean instant death. You have two choices – do you persuade Crudo to return to the 'Now Time' with you (go to 8) or do you take on the villainous Terrorsa-may yourself (go to 9)?

8 You return to the 'Now Time' with Crudo (invisible by your side) and you redistribute the stolen sterling. The kindfulness you receive in return galvanises your burgeoning beliefs and you become the leader of a good and just political party, ruling fairly for many years. Your success in sharing the British pound equally in the past prevents the evil Empress Terrorsa-may from ever ruling in the future. Every so often, you high-five your invisible chum, but only when no one's looking!

9 You arrive at the main hall of a magnificent future-castle, Crudo at your side. Ahead of you is an almighty throne made from human skin. On the throne sits the most terrifying creature you've ever seen. Wizened and with dark piercing eyes of pure avarice – Empress Terrorsa-may! Crudo explains that the only thing that can defeat the Empress is an example of pure unselfishness. The husk-like dictator turns towards you and roars an unearthly screech of evil intent. Thinking quickly, you fashion a makeshift sling, using the last of your gardening twine. What was it Crudo said? Unselfishness. With all your might, you sling your only gobstopper unselfishly at the roaring monster's mouth, forcefully sharing it with her.

But just before the sugary ball enters her orifice, a piercing space laser fires from the Empress's eyes and turns it to dust. She turns her gaze towards you, training her death ray directly at your beard. You close your eyes and await your inevitable death when you hear Crudo screaming a pitiful war cry. Opening your eyes, you see that Crudo has dived in front of you, taking the full impact of the laser, sacrificing his life for you. His guts are strewn across the hall, his acid blood stains your linen suit.

You look up at Empress Terrorsa-may, who begins to shrivel and shrink into a pile of skin and hair. Crudo's act of unselfishness has saved you – and all humanity. With that the sun begins to shine and you become a good and just and equal leader of the 'Further Time', where you rule for many years, inwardly saddened by the death of your scaly erstwhile enemy turned best friend, Crudo.

THE END

PHILIP HAMMOND

WARP SPEED (LIGHT YEARS)	4.1(PH)
HOME PLANET	SKARO
NEMESIS LIFEFORM	HUMANS
THREAT TO UNIVERSE	46GB
HYPER-GUILE	SUPER-PROFICIENT
BINARY REFERENCE	011111011
WAR CRY	EXTERMINATE!
FEDER-RATING	6

JEREMY'S "AGIT-POP" THE BALLOON GAME

Somebody has muddled up all the Labour Party's real policy balloons with fake propaganda balloons, designed to negatively influence voters and undermine the electoral system.

Using Jeremy's special propaganda pricker, help the Labour Party restore public opinion by popping all the deceptive balloons. Can you guess which of Jeremy's rosy red policy balloons are real and which ones are fake?

We believe in a fair taxation scheme for the common good

The Union Jack will be scrapped in favour of a flag with a Battenberg-based design

The UK currency will be renamed 'The Gonk'

We will invest £250 billion over ten years in upgrading our economy

We believe that Russian Cossack dancing must be taught in all schools

All over-50s must wear their pants on the outside of their trousers

We will invest in our NHS, to give patients the modern, well-resourced services they need

We will ensure energy costs are affordable for consumers and businesses

SPACE CAPTAIN JEREMY HAS GONE FOR A SPACEWALK IN SPACE.

He needs to get back to the Labour Mothership in time for his socialist space lunch, but – oh no! – he's under attack from a fleet of evil Torybots!! Guide Jeremy safely back to his space comrades and save the day!

HYPAFAX 3580

NICOLA STURGEON

WARP SPEED (LIGHT YEARS)	3.78(PH)
HOME PLANET	TATOOINE
NEMESIS LIFEFORM	THE SITH
THREAT TO UNIVERSE	6GB
HYPER-GUILE	PROFICIENT
BINARY REFERENCE	0100100
WAR CRY	GEE-AKKA-MALAYO-GEE!
FEDER-RATING	-68

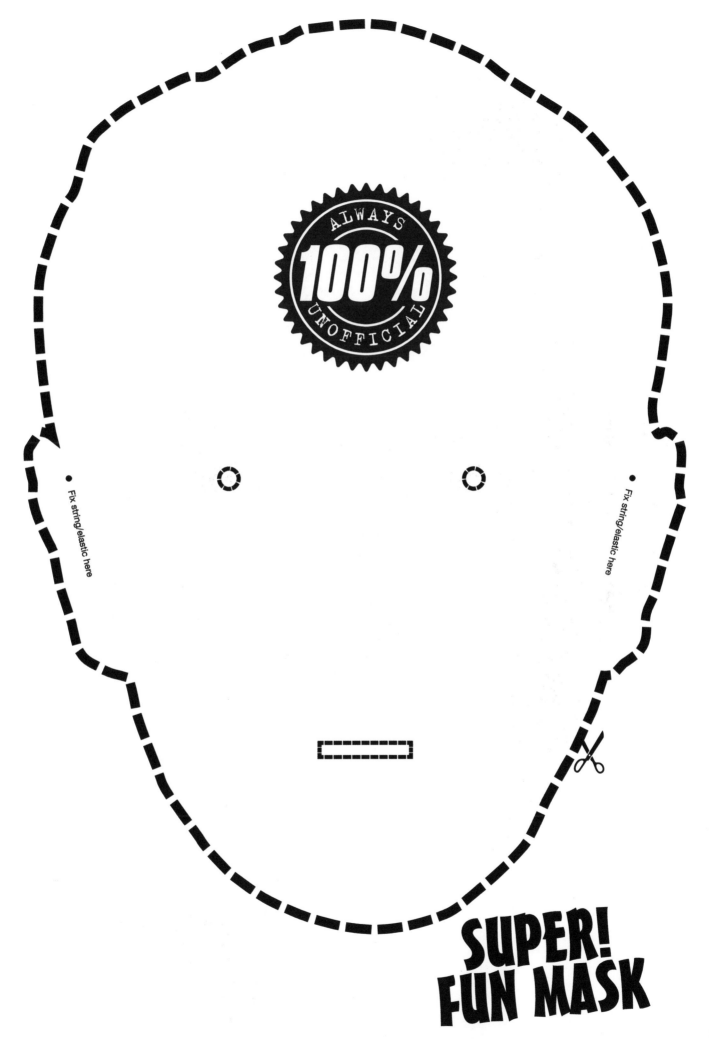

Fix string/elastic here

Fix string/elastic here

ALWAYS
100%
UNOFFICIAL

SUPER!
FUN MASK

SUPER!
FUN MASK

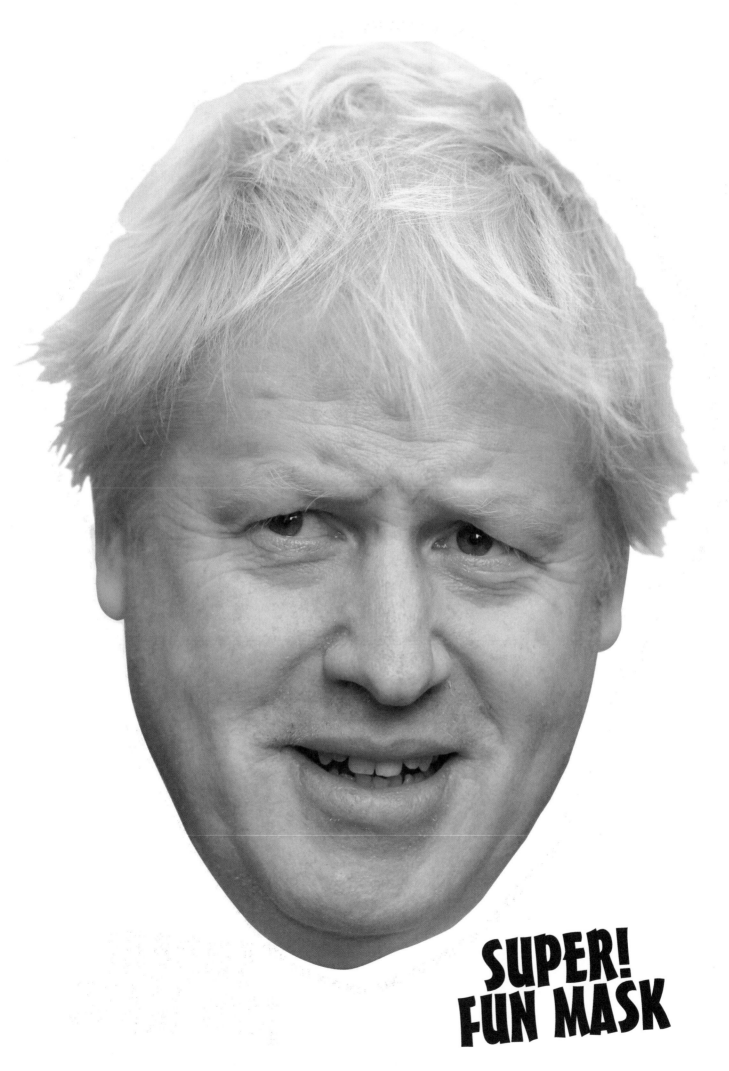

SUPER!
FUN MASK

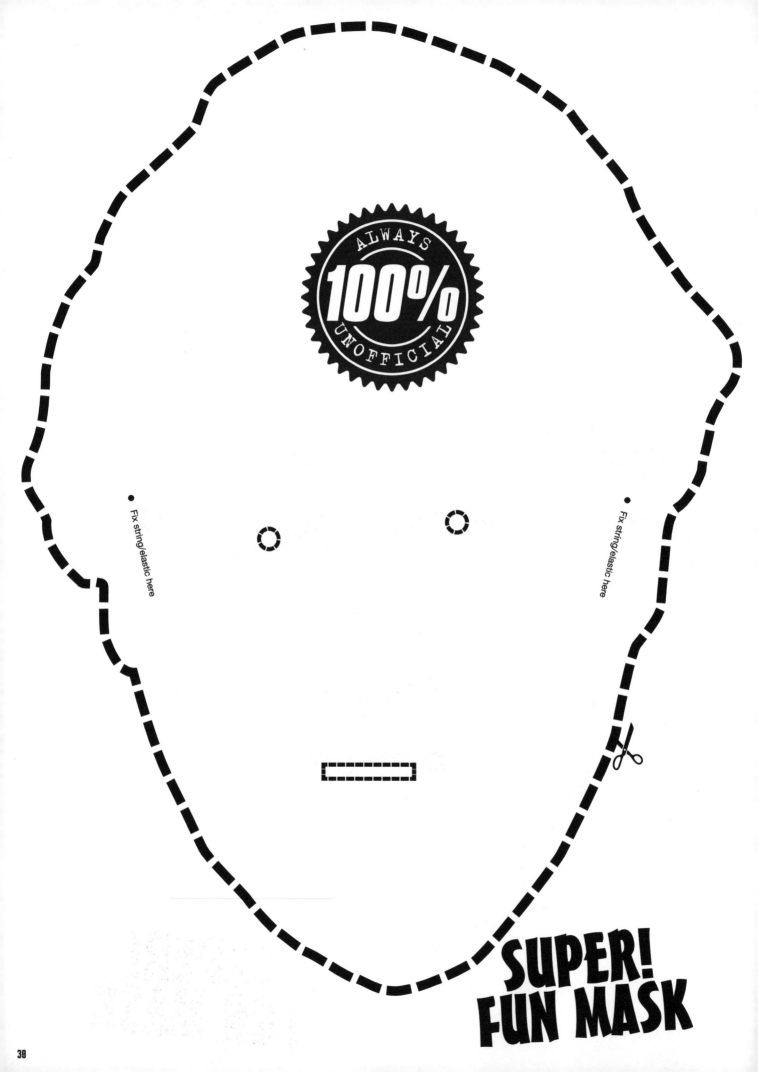

ALWAYS 100% UNOFFICIAL

Fix string/elastic here

Fix string/elastic here

SUPER! FUN MASK

38

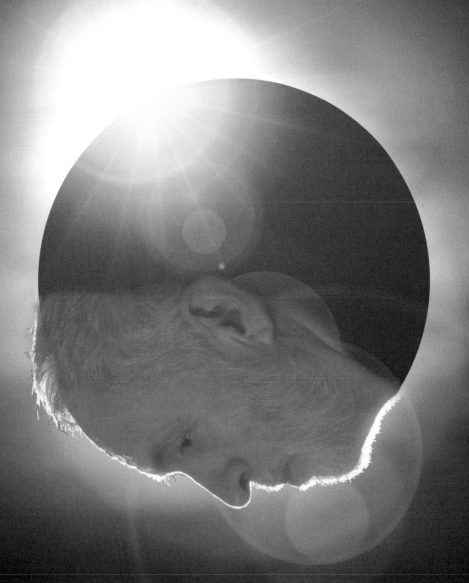

TOTAL ECLIPSE

OF MY HEART

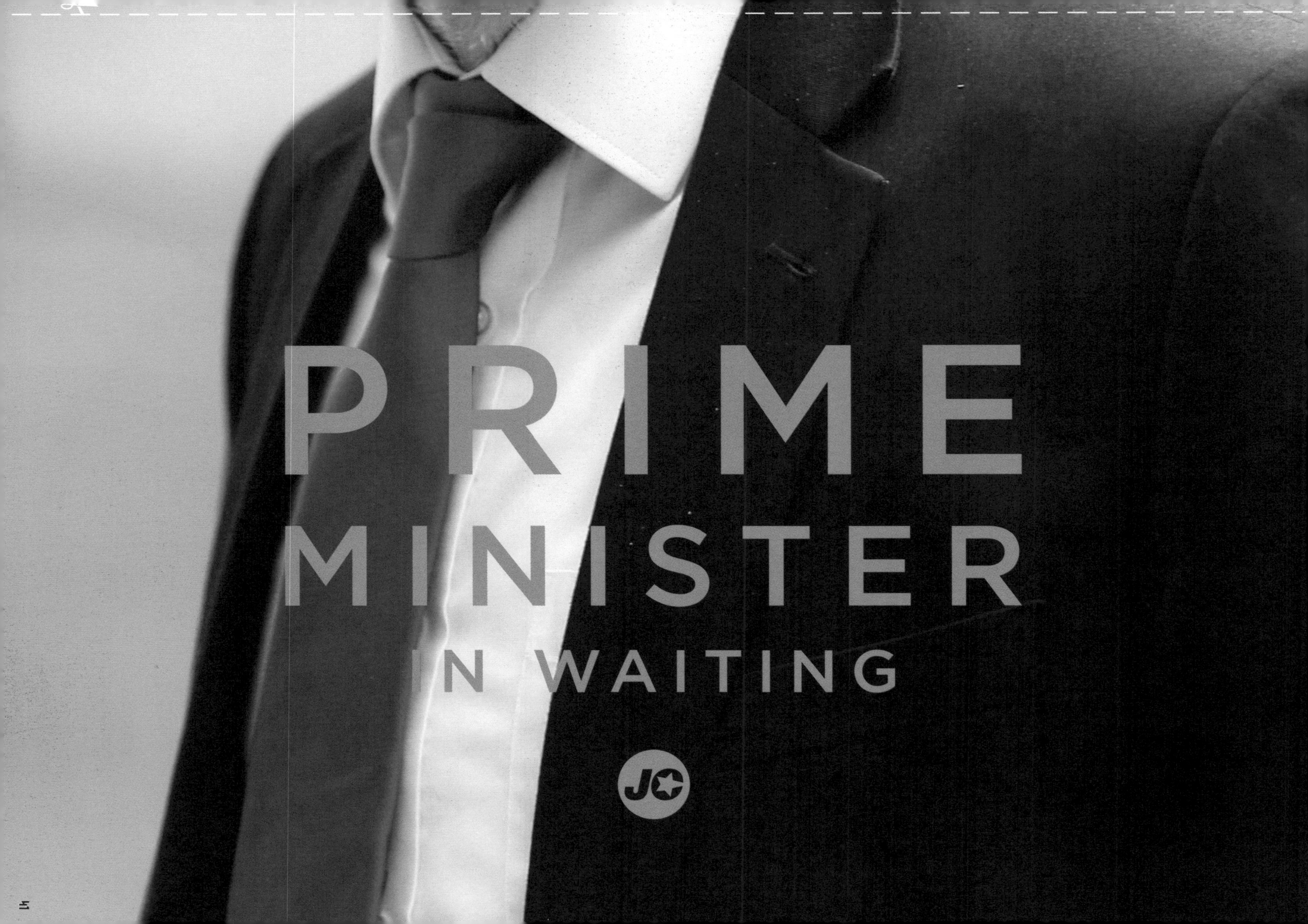

PRIME MINISTER IN WAITING

JO★

THUMBS UP FOR JEZZA!

HYPAFAX 4198

EMILY THORNBERRY

WARP SPEED (LIGHT YEARS)	6.7(PH)
HOME PLANET	KRYPTON
NEMESIS LIFEFORM	GENERAL ZOD
THREAT TO UNIVERSE	2.8GB
HYPER-GUILE	PROFICIENT
BINARY REFERENCE	000010101
WAR CRY	UM-LAK SHANHAH
FEDER-RATING	76

CORBYN'S AWESOME ARCADE

GALACTIC SOCIALOID INVADERS
VIDEO GAME

IF YOU LIKE VIDEO GAMES, THEN YOU'LL LOVE JEREMY'S VERY OWN ARCADE VIDEO GAME THAT YOU CAN MAKE AND PLAY YOURSELF AT HOME. SIMPLY CUT OUT THE SPACESHIP [ABOVE] AND STICK IT TO THE END OF A PENCIL USING STICKY TAPE OR GLUE. NOW, STARTING FROM THE LEFT-HAND SIDE OF THE SCREEN, 'FLY' YOUR SHIP, AVOIDING THE ASTEROIDS, ALIENS AND OTHER SPACE OBSTACLES, BLEEPING AS YOU GO. CAREFUL! YOU ONLY HAVE THREE LIVES. EACH TIME YOU REACH THE RIGHT-HAND SIDE YOU LEVEL UP! NOW FLIP YOUR SHIP BACK TO THE LEFT AND LEVEL UP AGAIN! AND SO ON... READY PLAYER ONE? THEN INSERT YOUR COIN, AND AWAY YOU GO!

Jezza's Celestial Party Snacks

Star Sarnies

★ Spread two slices of brown bread with butter substitute

★ Now spread on your favourite sandwich filler. Like jam!

★ Place one slice on top of the other with the spread sides facing each other

★ Using a star-shape cutter, cut into star shapes

Yum! Star-shaped, yummy, jam, party goodness

Kidney Bean Moons

★ Soak 200g of dry kidney beans for at least 8 hours until they are soft

★ Mush them into a paste in a mixing bowl

★ Thoroughly mix in a tablespoon of strawberry jam

★ Now shape the paste into half-moon shapes and serve

Wow! Kidney-bean, jam, lunar loveliness

Everybody loves a party but what's a party without the food? Here are some of Jezza's possible party food tips that are suitable for a birthday party... or even a Labour party!

Houmous Halley's Comets

★ Take a tablespoon of houmous and place on a serving dish

★ Slice 3 peeled carrots into long tail shapes to represent the tail

★ Place the carrots onto the serving dish as if trailing from the houmous like a tail

★ For a sweet option mix some strawberry jam into the houmous

Cool! Houmousy, jammy, carroty, comet snacks

Venusian Vegan Vegetables

★ Peel and slice one carrot

★ Chop some broccoli into small asteroid shapes

★ Do the same with some cauliflower

★ Slice half a cucumber into rocket like shapes

★ Arrange neatly on a serving dish

★ Serve with strawberry jam

Hey! Venus, vegan, vegetable and jam tastiness

JEREMYS

**IF YOU LOVE JEREMY CORBYN,
HERE ARE EVEN MORE JEREMYS YOU MIGHT LIKE TO CONSIDER**

PAXMAN

Fingers on buzzers! Which 68-year-old fast-talking, no-nonsense TV presenter pax (packs) quite alot into every sentence? Clue: he's quite a (university) challenging character! (Answer: he's Jeremy Paxman).

RENNER

This 47-year-old hunk is actually an actor not a runner (renner). Don't upset this Jeremy or he'll avenge you with his bow and arrow (because he plays archery-mad Hawkeye in The Avengers (not the Hawkeye from MASH (that was Alan Alda))).

BRETT

Solving the identity of this (sadly dead) detective Jeremy is elementary, my dear Watson. Because, my dear Watson, it's Jeremy Brett, the dapper actor who played (arguably) the quintessential Sherlock Holmes (when he was alive).

You might have caught this fishy 62-year-old Jeremy Wade-ing onto your television screen late at night on ITV 4. He casts his (fishing) net wide, because he's a (river) monster TV presenter who likes to sling his (fishing) hook at big, scary fish.

WADE

FISHER

If Jeremy Wade was a fictitious waistcoat-wearing frog, he would be this 112-year-old amphibian Jeremy: Jeremy Fisher, the frog from The Tale of Mr. Jeremy Fisher by (human) author Beatrix Potter (because Jeremy Fisher also likes fishing).

CORBYN'S COSMIC CROSSWORD

CAN YOU HELP SPACE CAPTAIN JEREMY COMPLETE HIS SECRET MISSION TO SAVE THE WORLD WITH HIS SOCIALIST RAY GUN? DECIPHER THESE CLUES TO HELP JEREMY BEAT THE BLUE ALIEN INVADERS.

ACROSS

1 The technology used to propel Captain Jeremy's exoskeleton when on lunar missions (7)
4 Receptacle Captain Jeremy might keep his space wallet in (3)
5 What Captain Corbyn might give you if you made a mistake, an _ _ _ _ _ (6)
6 A small, mischievous devil or sprite found on Earth
7 Collective name for Captain Jeremy's 'shadow' friends when in his human form (7)
10 Very enthusiastic and passionate way of talking about Captain Jeremy's achievements (6)
12 You might take some of these in allegiance to Captain Corbyn (5)
13 Captain Jeremy's favourite planet (4)
14 Captain Jeremy's escape vehicle (3)

DOWN

1 The word used by Earthling Joey Essex to describe Captain Jeremy (4)
2 Captain Jeremy's middle name in Earth language (7)
3 When Captain Jeremy is in human form, this is the London Borough his constituency is in (9)
4 Abbreviation of nationality of Captain Jeremy when in Earthling form (4)
8 Hemp or jute fibre, impregnated with tar to caulk joints and seams in wooden ships. But not in Captain Jeremy's space-ship (5)
9 The tiny green insects that eat the space vegetables in Captain Jeremy's space allotment (5)
11 433 _ _ _ _ . Stony and elongated asteroid of the Amor group. Or primordial God of Love (4)

VINCE CABLE

WARP SPEED (LIGHT YEARS)	0.003(PH)
HOME PLANET	PANDORA
NEMESIS LIFEFORM	NONE
THREAT TO UNIVERSE	NOT APPLICABLE
HYPER-GUILE	NONE
BINARY REFERENCE	0000000
WAR CRY	NONE
FEDER-RATING	114

JEREMY CORBYN
AND THE RED PLANET

BY FRANKLIN GARAMOND

Naz and Kacey were both good kids from overlooked, marginalised sections of society. Kacey wanted to go to university to study science but couldn't because her parents weren't rich enough to foot the bill. Naz was an idealist, but had just lost his job due to cuts in public-sector spending. Since they both had a lot of time on their hands, they had started spending time together at a local municipal recycling centre, where they hung out amongst the junk, talked about life and dreamed of something more...

One day, Naz and Kacey were at the dump, idly playing catch with a ballcock from a rusty old disused water tank.

"You know, society doesn't have to be like this," said Naz. "What if the world was different? What if everyone played small but significant roles serving something beyond ourselves, like functioning cogs in some giant, marvellous machine?"

"Yeah," agreed Kacey. "We could all be totally equal and share everything, instead of being selfish."

Just then, Naz threw the ballcock to Kacey, who went to catch it, missed, and then watched it go whizzing off over her head. The ballcock bounced off a tall pile of stained mattresses, and landed somewhere out of view.

"I'll get it," said Kacey. Behind the mattresses was a battered-looking garden shed.

"Strange," said Kacey. "What's a garden shed doing in a municipal recycling centre?"

Naz joined her. "I'm sure that shed wasn't there before," he said. "Look! The door's open. The ballcock must've bounced inside!"

Cautiously, the disadvantaged friends entered the shed. Except, inside, it wasn't a shed at all. The room they had entered was brightly lit. It was glistening white and futuristic in a 1960s sort of way, with a strange console of some kind in the centre that was covered in buttons and levers and unfamiliar technology. BBC Radiophonics Workshop-style space-age noises could be heard humming and bleeping in the background.

"My eyes must be playing tricks on me," said Kacey. "I swear this place is slightly smaller on the inside than it is on the outside!"

"What the..." Naz was dumbfounded. "What is this place?"

"You are inside the JADSIS," said a voice.

The two disaffected youths turned to find themselves in the company of an eccentrically yet blandly dressed, non-threatening-looking elderly man.

"It stands for Jam And Democratic Socialism In Space," said the man. "Welcome to my spaceship."

Naz and Kacey exchanged a glance – this old codger must be off his rocker, they both thought. Just then, Naz spotted the buttons on the peculiar console.

"What does this one do?" he asked, reaching out with his hand.

"Don't touch that!" said the strangely electable old fellow. But it was too late. Naz had pressed the button. With a low electronic hum, the door to the outside world closed. Lots of lights flashed and pulsed around them, accompanied by another strange space noise that sounded a bit like someone running a front-door key along the bass string of a gutted piano. Eventually, the lights and noises stopped.

"What on Earth was that all about?" asked Kacey.

"Why would you assume you were on Earth?" asked the white-haired man, with a twinkle in his eye.

"I've had enough of this. Let's go, Kacey," said Naz, heading for the door.

"I wouldn't go out there if I was you," said the venerable old man. Ignoring him, Naz opened the door and stepped back out into the municipal recycling centre. Except the municipal recycling centre wasn't there any more. Instead, Naz found himself standing in the middle of an unfamiliar rocky barren red landscape. Kacey joined him.

"Woah!" she exclaimed. "Where did the dump go?"

"It didn't go anywhere," said the mysterious shed owner. "We did."

"Where are we, then?" asked Naz.

"When are we, more like," said the senior citizen. "The year is 2749 and this is the planet Mars."

"What a load of rubbish," said Kacey. "I study science – or I would do if someone scrapped tuition fees – and I know that's impossible, even for Elon Musk."

Just then, they spotted a group of metallic pepper-pot-shaped robots approaching them from a rocky outcrop. The robots surrounded the trio and pointed what looked like toilet plungers at them.

"I don't know about Mars, but these guys definitely aren't from Croydon," said Naz.

"Careful," said the silver-haired man. "These are the Thatcherites! The deadliest race in the galaxy. They take over worlds, then dismantle their welfare systems and slash public funding. Mars used to be a peaceful communist

planet before the Thatcherites assimilated it. Let me do the talking."

"Alien political views detected," said one of the robots in a harsh, grating voice. "Prepare to be assimilated!"

"Wait!" said the unconventional old man. "Have you considered reversing austerity cuts in favour of renationalising public utilities?"

The robots looked at each other, confused by the unusual-yet-ordinary-looking man's words.

"Does... not... compute..." said the leader. "Initiate assimilation!"

"Time for Plan B," said the curious teacher-like man with a wink. He held up Naz and Kacey's ballcock. Instantly, the robots began panicking.

"Alert! Alert! Doomsday device detected!" shrieked the leader.

"Catch!" said the grandfatherly man as he tossed the ballcock towards the robots. The evil Thatcherites retreated in terror. "Quick – while they're distracted. Back to the JADSIS!"

The trio ran back to the garden shed and closed the door behind them. The old man pulled a lever on the console and the flashing lights and wheezing noises started again.

"What happened there?" asked Kacey. "I thought we were goners for sure! Why were they so scared of the ballcock?"

"Simple," said the old man. "On their planet, all weapons look like plumbing equipment, so they thought it was an atomic grenade. If they knew me, they'd know

that I'm passionately against nuclear armament, the fools. You see, capitalists can seem terrifying, but they're easily defeated."

Back in Croydon, Naz and Kacey said their goodbyes to their new old friend. Naz shook the man's wrinkled hand.

"It's a shame you have to leave. If you were a politician, I'd definitely vote for you," said the suddenly re-engaged young man.

"Me too. You stand for everything I believe in," agreed Kacey.

"But I cannot stay," said the grey-bearded nonconformist. "There are countless other planets and timelines out there that are desperately in need of my wisdom and policies on progressive social reform." He turned to enter his space shed.

"Wait!" said Kacey. "You never told us your name!"

The elderly radical looked back at them with a smile.

"You can call me... The Comrade," he said. And with that, he tumbled off through space and time.

THE END

COMRADES OF THE LEFT BEARD-GROOMING TIPS

You might think that Jeremy Corbyn is the only left-wing superstar with a beard... but you'd be wrong! There's a rich history of beards and radical social reform working in hirsute harmony. Here's how to get a revolutionary new look and radically reform your very own facial hair!

THE LENIN

You'll need clippers for this one. Smoothat the sides and tapering to a fine tip on the chin, with wax to finish. With this style you'll Leningrad-uate to the big time.

THE KARL MARX

Anything goes. Think Father John Misty meets Santa Claus. No clippers, scissors or wax required – just let it all hang out! Marx out of ten? Eleven!!

THE FIDEL CASTRO

Deceptive one, this. Looks unkempt, as if your sideburns have met under your chin. But you'll need to carefully crop in line with the jawline. Then you'll be Havana great time!

THE CHE GUEVARA

This rebellious style looks carefree, but you'll need a steady hand with the clippers to curate that wispy tache and hair-free lower lip look. There's a lot more Che-ving than you think!

THE FRIEDRICH ENGELS

Engels' style is like the Marx, but with added walrus. Deceptively difficult to maintain. Must be shampooed, conditioned, brushed and waxed twice daily to achieve the original hipster look.

THE LEON TROTSKY

Similar to the Lenin, but offset by a full head of freshly blow-dried bouffant hair (see also Jon Pertwee's Doctor Who). Achieve this look and you'll be hot-to-trotsky!

THE JEREMY CORBYN

The classic. One length – grade 3. Just clip and go. A beard for the many, not for the few.

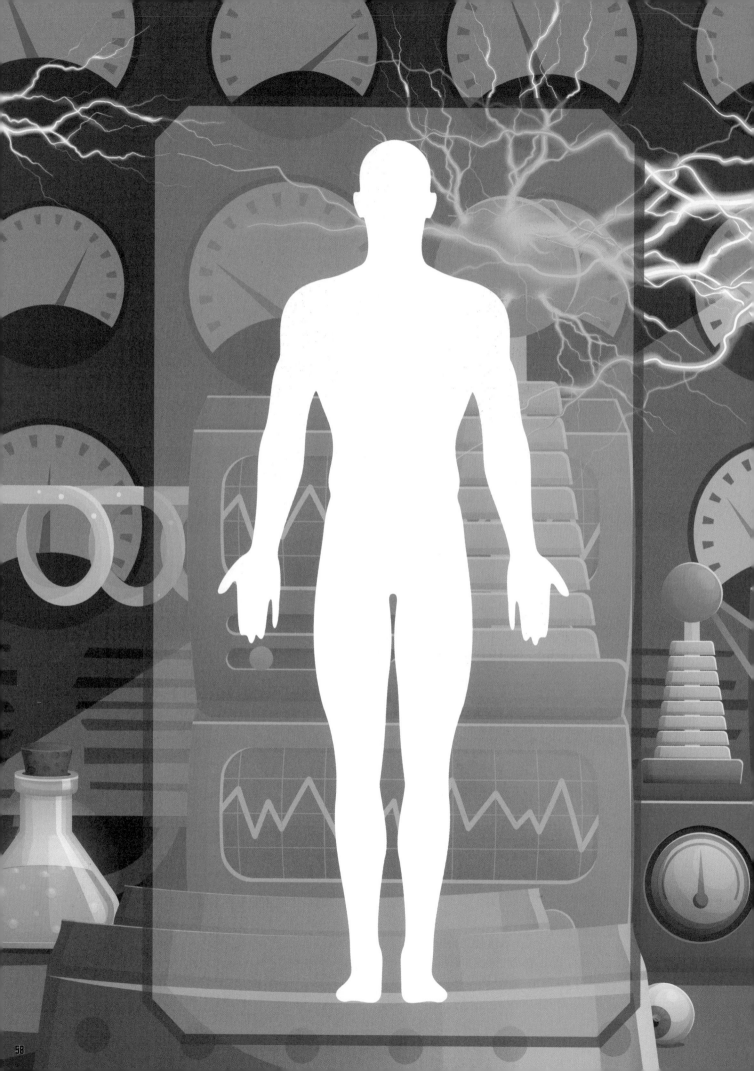

PROFESSOR CORBYNSTEIN'S LAB

Imagine you're Professor Corbynstein, a left-wing science genius. Cut out the body parts provided and 'splice' them together using sticky tape, to create the ultimate Labour politician.

The hairstyle of Diane Abbott

The eyebrows of Denis Healey

The beard of Jeremy Corbyn

The pipe of Tony Benn

The fists of John Prescott

The eyes of Tony Blair

The shoulders of Harriet Harman

The immune system of Nye Bevan

The feet of Michael Foot

The dancing hips of Ed Balls

MYSTIC JEREMY'S HOROSCOPE

As the brightest star in the political firmament, JC has had to keep his gaze fixed firmly on the future, but what if he could forecast your future for 2019 too? Using only the latest techniques and futuristic terminology, we predict what Jeremy would predict, if he were to predict your future.

ARIES

March 21 – April 19

Strong willed, ambitious and passionate

Your Mars bar is retraceable from its upgrade late June through later in later June. Life won't slow down. Mars bar retro in Aquarius and Copernicus encourages you to make your social life and work more sturdy.

FAMOUS POLITICAL ARIANS
Nigel Farage

TAURUS

April 20 – May 20

Generous, stubborn and selfish

When the sun enters Taurus, Venus is already there. Hello, there! In October, Venus goes direct to Libra (do not pass go) in November – not too good for your health!

FAMOUS POLITICAL TAUREANS
Vladimir Lenin

GEMINI

May 21 – June 20

Energetic, superficial and impulsive

Just after Venus de Milo turns lucid in November, your planet Mercury conjoins masterful Jupiter for five minutes flat. Your twin life needs more engagement at this juncture. Believe in yourself.

FAMOUS POLITICAL GEMINITES
Jeremy Corbyn

CANCER

June 21 – July 22

Loyal, moody, self-pitying

A massive bulbous lunar event in late July, just as Aquarius ascends the star space. Jupiter resists an emotional Scorpio from August backwards through August, making you ever more psychic.
Only blue on June 11th.

FAMOUS POLITICAL CANCERIAN
George W Bush

LEO
July 23 – August 22

Ambitious, domineering, melodramatic

Your Noodle Node is now in Leo now. Events up in
your life spin round and backbite in karmic reverse.
A partial solar eclipse in August could affect
your bowels. Prepare the prunes!

FAMOUS POLITICAL LEONS
Emily Thornberry

VIRGO
August 23 – September 22

Helpful, fussy, inflexible

Saturn is upper retrograde in Capricorn One from
April/June/July until early September/October/November.
Late August and early September will be much too electric times for you.

FAMOUS POLITICAL VIRGINS
Keir Starmer

LIBRA
September 23 – October 22

Peaceful, superficial, indecisive

The Venus principle isn't retrograde from Octoberfest
through the first minute and a half of November,
ending in Libra, impacts your tooth more. Love will reign supreme!

FAMOUS POLITICAL LIBRANS
Theresa May

SCORPIO
October 23 – November 21

Passionate, obsessive, suspicious

The all-splicing Mars-Neptune conglomerate in
Gemini may tug at your coat tails, but when Scorpio
gets going, the Sun is joined by Crockett and Tubbs. Jupiter and Mercury prizes
await!

FAMOUS POLITICAL SCORPIONS
Leon Trotsky

SAGITTARIUS
November 22 – December 21

Selfless, independent, unemotional

The sun conjoins your modern metal-loving planet, Bluto,
which is reasonable. All earth signs of Capricorn are gone,
my dear, leaving only despair and sorrow. Cheer up!

FAMOUS POLITICAL SAGITTARIANS
Billy Bragg

CAPRICORN
December 22 – January 19

Patient, dictatorial, distrusting

In the summer month of winter, Mars is retrospect in early Aquarius, and then
Apricorns, and then the other ones. Realign and reproduce great magnetic energy
here and now.

FAMOUS POLITICAL CAPRICOTS
Tom Watson

AQUARIUS
January 20 – February 18

Witty, unemotional, sarcastic

Your planet Uranus is making a slow transition
back and forth from time to time.
You will resonate well in Glasgow.

FAMOUS POLITICAL AQUARIUMS
Ronald Reagan

PISCES
February 19 – March 20

Compassionate, indecisive, self-pitying

Weak solar seeds prevent Mars from fluctuating and undulating during early
Thursday. Remove the lunar entry to facilitate a finer illusion of raucous with
Saturn. Try another year next year.

FAMOUS POLITICAL PESCETARIANS
Gordon Brown

STARRING
the young
HUGH GRANT
as the young
JEREMY CORBYN

A CONSERVATIVE AFFAIR

IT WAS 1985. GINA, JEREMY AND TERI WERE UNABLE TO SPEAK OF, HEAR OF, OR SEE OF THEIR TRUE FEELINGS!

Young Conservatives Teri and Gina always met at Tory HQ.

HI, GINA. LIKE MY NEW POSE?

WOW, TERI! THAT'S WELL COOL. THATCHER WOULD LOVE THAT!

They liked to practise their poses.

I LOVE BEING A 1980s TORY, DON'T YOU?

ME TOO! I LOVE THE IDEA OF BEING REALLY RICH. AND MARGARET THATCHER, THE LEADER OF THE CONSERVATIVE PARTY, IS MY HERO. NOTHING ON EARTH WOULD EVER MAKE ME LEAVE THE TORY PARTY.

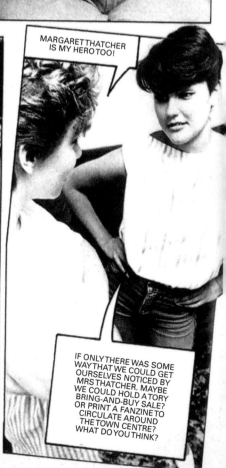

MARGARET THATCHER IS MY HERO TOO!

IF ONLY THERE WAS SOME WAY THAT WE COULD GET OURSELVES NOTICED BY MRS THATCHER. MAYBE WE COULD HOLD A TORY BRING-AND-BUY SALE? OR PRINT A FANZINE TO CIRCULATE AROUND THE TOWN CENTRE? WHAT DO YOU THINK?

NO! YOU KNOW THAT FANZINES MAKE ME SAD!

CHEER UP, CHIPSTICKS! WE'LL THINK OF SOMETHING! WE'RE TORIES!

I THINK I'VE JUST THOUGHT OF SOMETHING! IT'S RISKY BUT... WHAT IF WE WERE TO BRING DOWN THE LABOUR PARTY FROM THE INSIDE? YOU KNOW – GO UNDERCOVER!

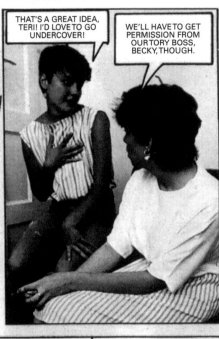

THAT'S A GREAT IDEA, TERI! I'D LOVE TO GO UNDERCOVER!

WE'LL HAVE TO GET PERMISSION FROM OUR TORY BOSS, BECKY, THOUGH.

Gina whispered in Becky's ear...

SHH! IT'S A SECRET! WE NEED YOUR PERMISSION TO GO DEEP UNDERCOVER!

Bug-eyed Becky had to get permission from **her** boss...

...Mrs Margaret Thatcher!

YES, MRS PRIME MINISTER. I MAKE SURE WE DON'T LOSE THEM TO SOCIALISM!

Meanwhile, at Labour HQ...

YOU HAVE A BRIGHT FUTURE IN THE LABOUR PARTY, JEREMY CORBYN, EVEN IF YOU DON'T HAVE A BEARD YET. LET'S PUT YOU IN CHARGE OF NEW RECRUITS.

SURE THING, TONY BENN! I LOVE THE LABOUR PARTY AND I LOVE NEW RECRUITS. I'LL BE GREAT AT RECRUITING THEM. AND I'LL THINK ABOUT THAT BEARD!

On the phone, Teri put on her best Labour accent...

OH, ER, HI... I WAS JUST WONDERING IF ME AND MY FRIEND COULD JOIN THE LABOUR PARTY? WE'RE NOT TORY SPIES OR ANYTHING!

HAHAHAHA! NO, I'M SURE YOU'RE NOT. YOU DON'T SOUND LIKE A TORY. MY NAME'S JEREMY, BY THE WAY.

WOW, HE SOUNDED REALLY HUNKY! BUT I WON'T TELL GINA OR SHE MIGHT TRY TO FALL IN LOVE WITH HIM OR SOMETHING UN-TORY LIKE THAT. I'LL HAVE TO GIVE HER A PEP TALK.

TOMORROW YOU'RE GOING IN DEEP UNDERCOVER, GINA. I DON'T WANT YOU MUCKING IT UP BY DOING ANY FALLING IN LOVE. YOU'RE A TORY!

THIS JEREMY CORBYN BLOKE SOUNDS LIKE A REAL THREAT. SO I WON'T BE DOING ANY FALLING IN LOVE! I'M A CONSERVATIVE THROUGH AND THROUGH!

GOOD, BECAUSE FALLING IN LOVE LEADS TO FRENCH KISSING AND FRENCH KISSING LEADS TO SOCIALISM. IF WE DON'T STOP CORBYN NOW, HE MIGHT ONE DAY BECOME LEADER OF THE LABOUR PARTY.

I LOVE FALLING IN LOVE BUT NOT AS MUCH AS I LOVE THE CONSERVATIVE PARTY

Next day...

SO YOU SEE, JEREMY, I DON'T EVEN EVER WANT TO HAVE MONEY... ANY MONEY I EVER DO HAVE, I KEEP FOR MYSELF...UM... I MEAN, I DISTRIBUTE IT EQUALLY.

GOOD. IF ONLY ONE PART OF SOCIETY HOLDS ALL THE WEALTH THERE'LL ALWAYS BE A DIVIDE BETWEEN RICH AND POOR.

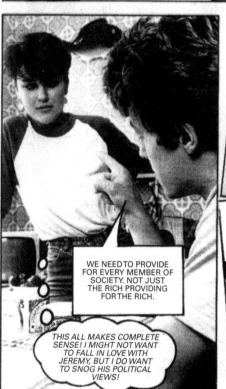

WE NEED TO PROVIDE FOR EVERY MEMBER OF SOCIETY. NOT JUST THE RICH PROVIDING FOR THE RICH.

THIS ALL MAKES COMPLETE SENSE! I MIGHT NOT WANT TO FALL IN LOVE WITH JEREMY, BUT I DO WANT TO SNOG HIS POLITICAL VIEWS!

YEAH... ER... IT WENT REALLY WELL. AND HE DEFINITELY DIDN'T CHANGE MY POLITICAL VIEWS AT ALL!

ARE YOU SURE? YOU LOOK DIFFERENT... SLIGHTLY LESS TORY SOMEHOW.

DON'T BE A DAFTY! I'M... JUST DEEP UNDERCOVER, REMEMBER! I'VE GOT TO LOOK REALLY LEFT WING, OR HE'LL TWIG.

CAREFUL! IF YOU GO TOO DEEP UNDERCOVER YOU MIGHT TURN RED!

I HOPE SHE'S NOT ONTO ME!

The girls decided to take a relaxing walk on some gravel and soon they were laughing like old Tory friends.

SO, GO ON, THEN, WHAT'S HE LIKE? IS THE FAMOUS JEREMY CORBYN REALLY AS DISHY AS PEOPLE SAY HE IS?

HE'S NOT BAD FOR A SOCIALIST. EVEN WITHOUT A BEARD.

I LOVE BEARDS, DON'T YOU? THEY'RE GREAT.

YEAH. I WISH THERE WAS A WAY TO DISTRIBUTE BEARDS EQUALLY, THOUGH.

WHAT WAS THAT? THAT SOUNDED LIKE LABOUR TALK!

ERM... ER... OH... NO! OF COURSE NOT! IT'S JUST COS I'M SO DEEP UNDERCOVER.

Blushing Gina was turning red on the outside and the inside!

UM... OBVIOUSLY I THINK THAT BEARDS SHOULD BE FOR RICH PEOPLE ONLY!

GOOD... COS I DON'T THINK MRS THATCHER WOULD APPROVE OF BEARDS BEING GIVEN AWAY ON THE NHS!

Two days later at Teri's...

HI, TERI, I JUST WANTED TO DROP BACK THESE TORY ALBUMS WE USED TO LISTEN TO TOGETHER. I'VE GOT SOME NEWS...

BUT PHIL COLLINS IS OUR FAVOURITE! 'NO JACKET REQUIRED' IS THE SEMINAL TORY ALBUM!

ACTUALLY, THERE'S SOMETHING I HAVE TO TELL YOU...

DON'T TELL ME. YOU'VE FALLEN FOR JEREMY CORBYN. YOU'VE BEEN HEAVY PETTING!

NO, TERI. I HAVEN'T FALLEN FOR JEREMY. BUT I HAVE FALLEN FOR HIS IDEOLOGY, AND TAKEN IT A STEP FURTHER. IN FACT...

...I'M DEFECTING TO THE SOVIET UNION. LOOK, HERE'S MY SPECIAL COMMUNIST PARTY RING.

FLIPPING HECK, GINA! WHAT DO YOU THINK YOU'RE FLIPPING PLAYING AT?

EXCUSE MY FRENCH BUT I'M REALLY FLIPPING CROSS!

I'M CATCHING THE 5.15 TRAIN TO MOSCOW. SEE YA, COMRADE!

Teri sat down on a couch...

FLIPPING COMMUNISM, FLIPPING MOSCOW! WELL, THAT DIDN'T GO TO PLAN! WE HAVEN'T BROUGHT DOWN THE LABOUR PARTY FROM WITHIN AND MARGARET THATCHER HASN'T NOTICED ME YET. THIS CORBYN GUY'S GOOD.

RIGHT. I'VE GOT MY CARDIGAN ON AND I MEAN BUSINESS! I'LL DEAL WITH THIS MYSELF!

Jeremy was relaxing with some red, red wine...

HI, JEREMY, I'M THE OTHER NEW RECRUIT AND I REALLY WANT TO LEARN ABOUT LABOUR.

WHAT HAPPENED TO GINA? SHE WAS DOING REALLY WELL HERE.

SHE'S DEAD. DEAD TO ME, ANYWAY. LET'S JUST SAY SHE'S TURNED REDDER THAN YOUR RED, RED WINE. ANYWAY, FORGET ABOUT GINA. I'M HERE TO UNDERMINE – I MEAN SUPPORT LABOUR ANY WAY I CAN.

GREAT. WELL, DO YOU WANT TO HEAR ABOUT SOME OF OUR POLICIES?

SURE THING. CAN I JUST SAY HOW MUCH I HATE THOSE TORIES? ESPECIALLY MY HERO, MARGARET THATCHER.

ME TOO!

HEY, DO YOU WANT TO HEAR A JOKE ABOUT TORIES? HOW MANY TORIES DOES IT TAKE TO CHANGE A LIGHTBULB? NONE – THEY GET THE PROLETARIAT TO DO IT FOR THEM!

HEY, DO YOU WANT TO KISS ME?

WELL, I HADN'T THOUGHT OF THAT BEFORE, BUT NOW YOU MENTION IT, THERE IS SOMETHING ABOUT YOU. SOMETHING DANGEROUS… FORBIDDEN, EVEN.

TERI, I DON'T KNOW WHO YOU ARE OR WHERE YOU COME FROM, BUT IN THE SHORT TIME WE'VE BEEN TOGETHER, I'VE FALLEN MADLY IN LOVE WITH YOU!

HAHA! YOU'RE IN LOVE WITH ME, JUST AS I INTENDED. BUT NOW I'M GOING TO BREAK YOUR HEART, JUST LIKE YOU BROKE MY FRIEND'S MIND! I COULD NEVER LOVE YOU. YOU HAVEN'T EVEN GOT A BEARD! GOODBYE JEREMY.

Teri whispered her success to her Tory boss's ear…

SHHH! IT'S A SECRET, BUT WELL DONE. MRS THATCHER HAS HEARD OF YOUR SUCCESS AND WANTS TO MEET YOU. IN SECRET. THE TORY BIKE SHEDS, HALF AN HOUR.

SHHH! THANK YOU, BECKY. MRS THATCHER WANTS TO MEET ME? I CAN'T BELIEVE IT. I'LL WEAR MY BEST V-NECK!

Behind the Tory bike sheds…

YES, MRS THATCHER, IT **IS** MY AMBITION TO BECOME AN MP AND, MAYBE ONE DAY, A LADY PRIME MINISTER, LIKE YOU.

I CAN'T BELIEVE I JUST MET MY HERO, MARGARET THATCHER, BEHIND THE TORY BIKE SHEDS!

A **CORBYN** LOVE STORY

AND AS FOR POOR OLD JEREMY CORBYN, I THINK I CAN SAFELY SAY I'VE BROKEN HIS HEART AND PUT PAID TO HIS CAREER!

AS FOR ME, I THINK I'VE GOT A STRONG AND STABLE CAREER AHEAD OF ME OR MY NAME'S NOT TERI… SHORT FOR **THERESA MAY**!!

SEE YOU IN 2016, FOLKS!

THE END

KEIR STARMER

WARP SPEED (LIGHT YEARS)	0.015(PH)
HOME PLANET	HOTH
NEMESIS LIFEFORM	DRACONS
THREAT TO UNIVERSE	7GB
HYPER-GUILE	PROFICIENT
BINARY REFERENCE	110110
WAR CRY	KLAK-KLAK!
FEDER-RATING	91

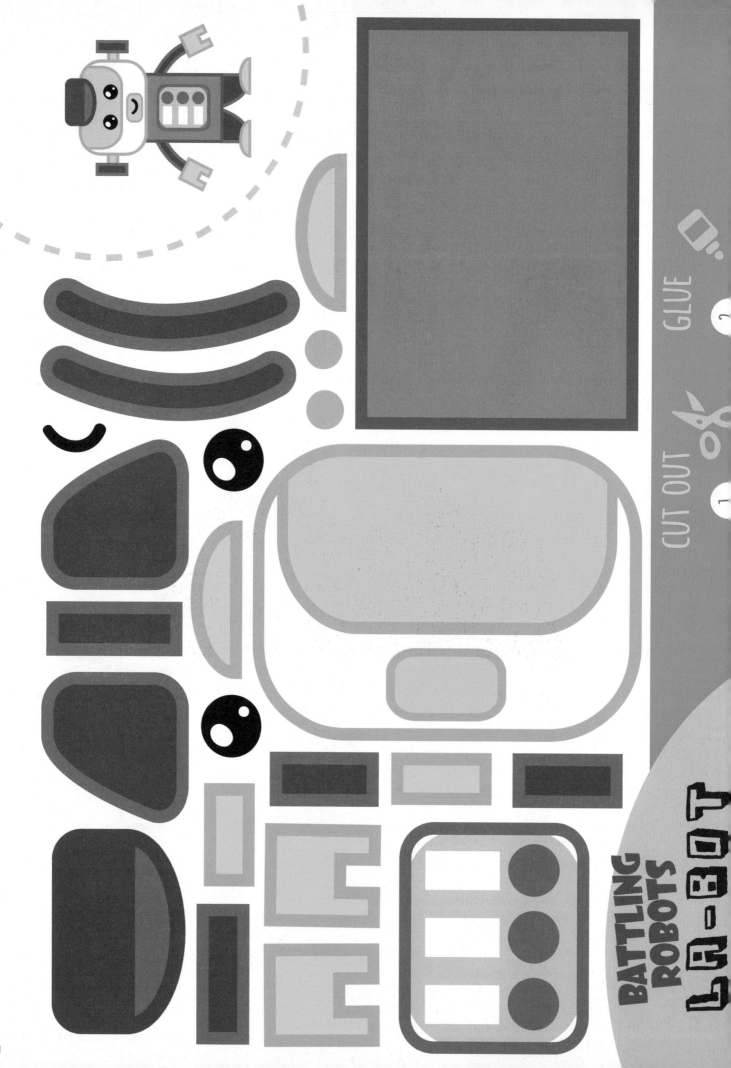

CUT OUT

GLUE

1 2

BATTLING ROBOTS
LA-BOT

COMPLETE YOUR ROBOTS
AND LET BATTLE COMMENCE!

CORBYN'S SNAILS 'N' ADDERS BOARD GAME

11 12 13 14 15 16 17 18 19 20 21 22 23

9 8 7 6 5

1 2 3

START

SPACE FLEET CAPTAIN JEREMY CORBYN'S SPACE SNAILS HAVE ESCAPED FROM HIS SPACE ALLOTMENT!

And they're going to get eaten by these evil space adders unless someone rounds them up. As one of Jeremy's brightest cadets, be the first to fly your space pod to the allotment to help him. If you land on a snail, boost forward two spaces. But watch out! If you land on an adder, you'll have to slide all the way down its slippery back!

READERS FAN ART!

Hey, Gang!

Here at 'Corbyn Annual Towers', we get some really great fan art sent in by you guys, and rather than keeping it all to ourselves to pore over we thought we might share some of that amazing talent with you at home!

Fancy yourself as a prototype Picasso or a trainee Tony Hart? Then why not grab some pencils and some paper and create your very own Jezza-based masterpiece. If you send it to us here*, and we think it's good, then you may very well find your pic included** in next year's awesome 'Unofficial Jeremy Corbyn Annual'!

Best,

The Editor

*Please send your art to the Unofficial Jeremy Corbyn Annual Readers Fan Art Submissions, 43 Great Ormond Street, London, WC1N 3HZ. Please include your name and address, and unfortunately we cannot return your art to you.

Sherlock Corbyn
Graham, aged 44, Liverpool

ELEMENTARY MY DEAR TOM WATSON.

Jeremy Corbyn
Amanda, aged 49, Salford

SUPER — CORBYN!

Super Corbyn
Arthur, aged 9, Glasgow

Dirtbike

Dirtbike
Elliot, aged 13, Coventry

IT'S JAM O'CLOCK!

The Jam Man
Harold, aged 10, London

The Surfer
Albert, aged 11, Chelmsford

A
REVOLUTIONARY
ROMANCE

BY
MILSON BOONE

Drusilla was a lowly but sensual young chambermaid who worked in the Palace of Westminster, serving the chambers of Prince Jeremy, the brooding, powerful, bearded older man who would one day be the ruler of all the land.

But Prince Jeremy wasn't like any other prince Drusilla had ever seen. He wasn't gluttonous, flamboyant or inconsiderate like other members of the ruling classes. Instead, he was generous, respectful and driven by a passion to help others. Prince Jeremy believed in change. In fact, he didn't believe in the ruling classes at all and had vowed to revolutionise everything when he came to power, so that there were no longer any inequalities between people, regardless of who they were or where they came from. Often, Drusilla would watch him admiringly when he thought she wasn't looking, feeling butterflies in her tummy as she quietly observed him ardently carrying out acts of benevolence as she dusted his candlesticks.

While she carried out her daily chambermaidly duties, Drusilla frequently found herself innocently dreaming of what it would be like to be Prince Jeremy's lover. She imagined his strong arms around her, his beard brushing against her soft cheek, his commanding voice whispering sweet nothings in her ear: "Oh, my darling Drusilla, a fair taxation system would mean that higher wage earners would pay more for public services." But she

quickly dismissed these thoughts. After all, he was a prince and she was just a lowly but sensual chambermaid.

Then, one day, Drusilla was polishing the prince's bedknobs when she heard a manly cry from the bathroom. Without thinking, she dropped her chamois and rushed to help. She entered the ornate washroom and discovered to her horror that Jeremy had cut himself whilst trimming his neck hair – the tip of his left forefinger was dripping with crimson blood. Instinctively, Drusilla took his wounded hand and clutched it to her bosom, then began bandaging it with some cloth that she ripped from the hem of her chambermaid's bodice.

It took her a moment to realise that she held his hand in hers. It felt powerful and masculine in her own soft embrace – a tough but fair hand. A hand that believed in free healthcare for all, as well as legislation that challenged discrimination of all kinds. With his hand skin against hers, her heartbeat raced and she felt a surge of erotic electricity passing through her entire body.

"Thank you," said Prince Jeremy, warmly.

His words jolted her back to reality; suddenly, Drusilla was aware that, through her actions, she had crossed an invisible barrier that separated their worlds.

"I… I'm sorry – I shouldn't have touched your hand skin. I am but a lowly chambermaid," she stuttered.

"There's no need to apologise," said the prince, assertively yet softly. "In my mind, you are not a lowly chambermaid. We are exactly the same, you and I and, if it were up to me, I would introduce a series of reforms aimed at addressing social inequalities like these, as well as invest more in underfunded services, such as education and policing."

Every night, from then on, Drusilla would lie awake and relive the moment she and the prince had shared, daring to dream that, one day, they might be able to hold each other's hand skin once again… or maybe something more…

And then something miraculous began to happen. As before, Drusilla would steal glances at the handsome prince when she thought he wasn't looking. But now, every so often, the prince would return her gaze with an ardent glance of his own in her direction. These moments were always unspoken, but charged with immense sexual power, as if the dam of erotic desire could at any moment burst and drown the pair in a flood of carnal release.

These brief, clandestine flirtations did not go unnoticed, however. Suzie, Drusilla's jealous co-worker, caught the prince and his chambermaid exchanging longing looks on more than one occasion. Harbouring a secret crush on the passionate prince herself, Suzie took her revenge by reporting Drusilla to the chief chambermaid, Mrs Curmudgeon. Before she knew it, Drusilla was told to report to her superior's office.

"It has come to our attention that you are guilty of indulging in an inappropriately sexual glancing relationship with Prince Jeremy," said the stern Mrs Curmudgeon sombrely.

"But we haven't done anything! I just bandaged his hand when he cut it trimming his neck hair!" protested Drusilla.

"It doesn't matter. In our country, the ruling classes and the workers must never consort with each other in any way, even with just their eyes and their hands. It is forbidden."

"Then our country is stupid," said Drusilla.

"Perhaps," said Mrs Curmudgeon, with a curious wistful sadness in her eyes. "Nevertheless, it is my duty to banish you from this palace. You must never set foot here again!"

With a heavy heart, Drusilla collected her meagre belongings and left the palace via the chambermaid's exit. As she walked towards the gates with tears in her eyes, she turned and looked back with great yearning at the prince's bedchamber window, where she had served for so many years. She thought she saw a familiar, imposing yet compassionate, bearded face watching her leave. But when she blinked her tears away, the face had gone. "Just wishful thinking," she thought to herself as she left the palace grounds and returned to the slums on the working-class side of town.

Many years passed. Drusilla tried to forget Prince Jeremy, but the fires of desire still burned deep within her body and her mind,

and none of the other boys she met ever made her feel the same irrepressible raw, erogenous swell that she had felt whenever she was in Jeremy's presence. Prince Jeremy was now Prime Minister Jeremy, having been democratically elected the ruler of all the land. Just as he had promised, Jeremy had dismantled the mechanisms of oppression and established a fairer society that upheld social justice, equal rights and trade unionism.

As a result of Jeremy's reforms, Drusilla had been able to go back to school, even though she was poor, and she had retrained as an important engineer. No longer was she a bashful young girl with butterflies in her tummy – Drusilla had blossomed into a strong, independent young woman. "Still, Jeremy's sure to be far too busy being a benevolent socialist leader to bother with an ex-chambermaid like me," Drusilla told herself.

But then, one stormy night, when the rain fell hard on her council house roof, Drusilla was awakened by a powerful yet compassionate knocking at her door. "Who could that be at this time of night?" she asked herself as she pulled on her night robe. A deep roll of thunder seemed to be trying to answer her question…

Drusilla opened her front door and a flash of lightning lit up the face of the man who stood there. Drusilla couldn't believe her eyes! It was Prime Minister Jeremy himself – his kindful eyes smiling at her and his beard streaked with rain.

"I believe this belongs to you," he said as he knelt down onto one knee.

Jeremy was holding something out towards her – she tore her gaze away from his handsome face to look down and, to her disbelief, saw that it was the ripped hem of the bodice she had used to bandage his finger. He had kept it all these years! Drusilla reached out to take the small piece of material. And when her hand skin met his once again, the waves of passion that she had been keeping locked up inside her for what seemed like an eternity finally came crashing out in a glorious rush, increasing in throbbing spirals of warm intensity that rippled through her body like an earthquake of ecstasy…

"Anyway, just wanted to return that to you. Hope you're keeping well!" And with that the handsome former prince turned on his heels and bid adieu forever.

THE END

JACOB REES-MOGG

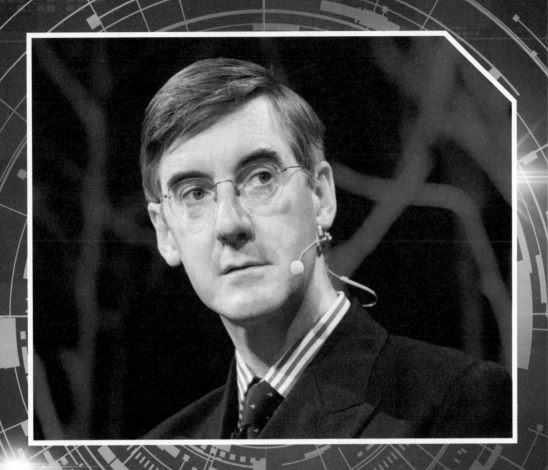

WARP SPEED (LIGHT YEARS)	0.76(PH)
HOME PLANET	URANUS
NEMESIS LIFEFORM	DUCKS
THREAT TO UNIVERSE	12.6GB
HYPER-GUILE	PROFICIENT
BINARY REFERENCE	000100001
WAR CRY	TALLY-HO!
FEDER-RATING	13

ANSWERS!

CORBYN'S COSMIC CROSSWORD

```
R O B O T I C   . B A G .
E . E . . S . . R . . . .
E A R F U L . . R I M P .
M . N . . L . . . T . . .
O . C A B I N E T . A . .
A . R . . G . . . . P . .
A R D E N T . . O A T H S
K . R . . O . . . . I . .
U . . . . N . P O D . . .
M A R S . . . . . . . . .
```

CORBYN TREK – THE SEARCH FOR WORDS (SEARCH)

```
M A R X U E W S L E G N E
C Z J Y T A S T E R O I D
O S H R O P S H I R E F U
R X S W P W F S B E A R D
L K M I D A O I E E Q C
I R I A B P C W C D N Y
N M S I L A I C O S A
E L E F T H E S N K I B
C N R O C K E T E O I B A
E T U J V T W Y E M N A F
J A M I L L E T R Y D F J
P R O L E T A R I A T O D
M O G G M W E L F A R E V
```

ANSWERS!

REES-MOGGIES ON THE LOOSE GAME

Those pesky Rees-Moggies were hidden on:

Page 8	Page 17	Page 21
Page 24	Page 30	Page 45
Page 48	Page 56	Page 61
Page 70	Page 71	Page 72

JEREMY'S 'AGIT-POP' THE BALLOON GAME

The fake balloons that were designed to negatively influence voters and undermine the electoral system were:

All over-50s must wear their pants on the outside of their trousers

The UK currency will be renamed 'The Gonk'

We believe that Russian Cossack dancing must be taught in all schools

The Union Jack will be scrapped in favour of a flag with a Battenberg-based design

CREDITS

The photostories 'Possessed by Love' and 'A Conservative Affair' originally appeared in My Guy magazine and can be seen in their original 1980s form in *The Best of My Guy* by Frank Hopkinson (ISBN 9781861059796).

Proofreading: Ian Allen (ianallen224@gmail.com)

PHOTO CREDITS

Alamy.com: page 20, Robert Melen; page 39, Matthew Chattle; page 49 (top), AF archive; page 49 (middle), WENN Ltd; page 67, Tommy London; page 77, keith morris news.

Shutterstock.com: page 7 (bottom right), twocoms; page 8 twocoms; page 14, twocoms; page 16, twocoms; page 23, twocoms; page 24 (top), twocoms; page 24 (bottom), Jim Wood; page 25 (top), twocoms; page 25 (bottom), twocoms; page 29, twocoms; page 30, twocoms; page 32, twocoms; page 34, Jonathan Mitchell Images; page 36, twocoms; page 37, twocoms; page 40, twocoms; page 42, 1000 Words; page 43, Ms Jane Campbell; page 48 (top), landmarkmedia; page 48 (bottom), Ga Fullner; page 52, Lingtren Images; page 56 (top), Everett Historical; page 56 (bottom left), Everett Historical; page 56 (bottom right), Rob Crandall; page 57 (top left), severjn; page 57 (top right), Uncle Leo; page 57 (bottom left), Olga Popova; page 57 (bottom right), twocoms; page 59, twocoms.

ACKNOWLEDGEMENTS

Thanks to Ian Allen for his continued excellence in the field of proofreading and copy-editing. And for the occasional gratis pun!